TOTAL ECLIPSE
OF THE SUN
COAST TO COAST USA

BY PAM HINE

www.mascotbooks.com

Total Eclipse of the Sun: Coast to Coast USA

Every effort has been made to ensure that all the information in this book is accurate and correct. The author and publisher assume no responsibility for any injury, loss or damage caused or sustained as a consequence of the use and application of this book.

This book may be ordered from: mascotbooks.com or amazon.com

For more information, please contact:
Mascot Books
560 Herndon Parkway #120
Herndon, VA 20170
info@mascotbooks.com

First Edition

CPSIA Code: PRT1216A
ISBN-13: 978-1-63177-932-9

Printed in China

CONTENTS

A PREDICTION

*It is predicted that during broad daylight on
Monday, August 21, 2017, darkness will descend on parts
of the United States as the Sun gradually becomes a smaller and
smaller crescent of light. The air temperature will drop,
birds will stop singing, and animals and plants will
behave as if night is coming.*

*With a sudden swoop of shadow,
the Sun will disappear completely.*

Fortunately, it is also predicted that after a couple of minutes of darkness, the Sun will gradually reappear and normal life will resume. In ancient times, the event would have been heralded as a sign of the gods' displeasure or a precursor of catastrophe. However, through the scientific study of the solar system, we know today that this extraordinary phenomenon is actually a total eclipse of the Sun.

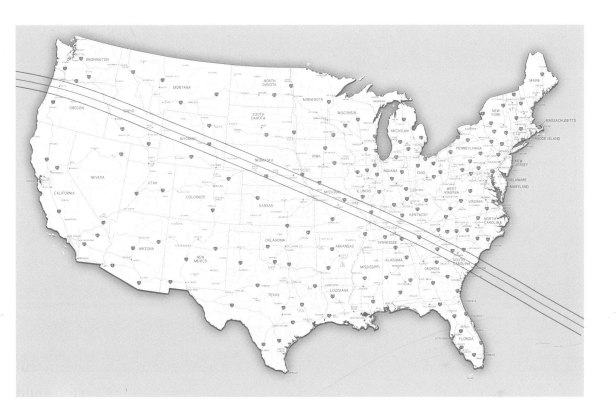

Millions of people across the country will experience the total eclipse of the Sun on August 21, 2017. The *path of totality* (the path of the *umbra*, or the area where you will be able to witness the total solar eclipse) traces a corridor about 65 miles wide. It makes landfall on the coast of Oregon, travels for around 2,500 miles across the central United States, and ends in the Atlantic Ocean off the coast of South Carolina.

WHAT IS AN ECLIPSE?

An eclipse of the Sun happens when the Moon moves between the Earth and the Sun so that the three bodies are in line. From Earth, it appears as though the Moon masks the Sun. If the Moon covers the Sun completely, it is a total eclipse. If the Sun is only partly obscured, it is a *partial eclipse*. The area of Sun eclipsed by the Moon is termed the percentage of *obscuration*.

The central area of dark shadow, from which a total eclipse is seen, is called the *umbra*. The much larger area of shadow surrounding the umbra is called the *penumbra*, from which a partial eclipse is seen. Within the penumbra, the depth of shadow reduces gradually from the edge of the umbra to the outside edge, reflecting the extent to which the Sun is covered by the Moon.

This diagram opposite illustrates what happens when the Sun, Moon and Earth align (not to scale).

By a remarkable coincidence, the Sun and Moon appear to be almost the same size when viewed from the Earth. The orbits of the Moon around the Earth and the Earth around the Sun are elliptical, rather than circular. Consequently, the apparent sizes of the Sun and Moon change. Sometimes the Moon appears to be smaller than the Sun, and sometimes it appears larger, depending on its position in orbit. It is only when the Moon appears larger than the Sun that a total eclipse is possible.

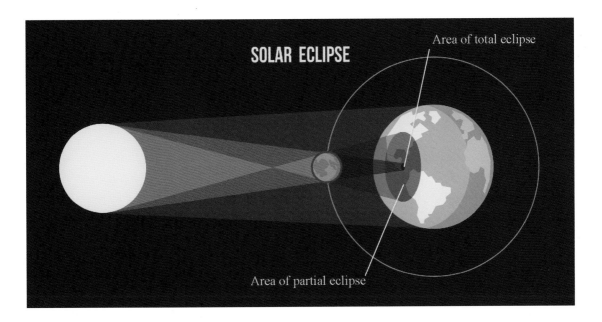

SOLAR ECLIPSE

Area of total eclipse

Area of partial eclipse

The Sun's movement across the sky is common knowledge. Day after day, it rises in the East and sets in the West. However, many people are less aware of the motion of the Moon. In fact, it follows a similar path across the sky to that of the Sun, only slightly slower. It takes just under 25 hours, from moonrise to moonrise. These apparent movements of the Sun and Moon are due mainly to the rotation of the Earth on its axis, and also to the movement of the Earth around the Sun and the Moon around the Earth.

Although the Moon is not very noticeable during daylight, it is present in the daytime sky for, on average, half of the time. Once every 29 days or so, at the time of the New

Moon (when the Moon is not visible to us as it is only illuminated on the far side), the Sun "laps" the Moon. It usually passes above or below it, but when the Sun passes behind the Moon, there is an eclipse of the Sun.

The orbital plane of the Moon around the Earth lies at an angle of about five degrees to the orbital plane of the Earth around the Sun. For the three bodies to line up sufficiently for an eclipse, the Moon must be close to the line of intersection of these planes. Because of this, eclipses are relatively rare.

A total eclipse of the Sun occurs on average somewhere on Earth about once every 18 months. However, any one point on the Earth will be in the path of totality on average once every 360 years. The last total eclipse visible from the Continental United States occurred in 1979, and the next will be in 2024—it will not be too long before the next total eclipse in the United States.

In contrast, a *lunar eclipse* (eclipse of the Moon) happens at the time of Full Moon when the Sun and Moon are on opposite sides of the Earth. A *total lunar eclipse* is seen much more often than a *total solar eclipse* – firstly because the Earth casts a much larger shadow than the Moon and secondly because a lunar eclipse can be seen by everyone on the dark side of the Earth.

On August 21, 2017, people in the path of totality will experience a spectacular phenomenon—probably the most awe-inspiring light show in the world.

In the partial phase, it will appear as if a small bite was taken out of the right hand side of the Sun—make sure to use special protective viewers. Very slowly, over the next hour or so, the bite will become bigger and bigger, and the air temperature will start to drop as the light levels reduce.

It will become darker more rapidly as the crescent Sun diminishes to a fine line. It may feel as if a bad storm is approaching. But with no sign of rain clouds, the dark sky can still be disconcerting. An eerie silence will descend as animals and birds assume their nighttime behaviors. Flowers may begin to close their petals. As the umbra approaches, the sky on the western horizon will darken. The Sun's crescent will reduce to a string of bright beads of light as the last rays shine between the mountains of the Moon. These are known as *Baily's Beads*.

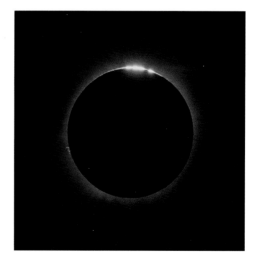

One by one, the beads will rapidly disappear. When only one remains, the result is the stunning effect known as the "diamond ring."

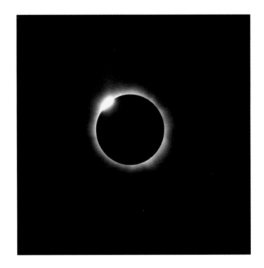

When the last bead is gone, it will be safe to look toward the Sun without protective viewers. *Totality* descends with a startling shock quite unlike anything else ever experienced. We will be faced with an awesome and extraordinary sight: a large black disc where the Sun should be, and around it the Sun's magnificent *corona* will extend several Sun-diameters out into space, like petals on a giant cosmic flower. This has been called the "Eye of God."

At the edge of the Moon, the Sun's *chromosphere* (literally sphere of color) will appear briefly as a thin crescent of red light. The occasional *prominence* may protrude from the Sun's surface. Stars and planets should become visible in the middle of the day.

When Baily's Beads begin to reappear, the magical phase of totality is over and it is time to replace your eye protection. Your relationship with the Sun will never be the same again! It is an extraordinary experience which people will remember for the rest of their lives.

<u>**Only the people within the path of totality will witness a Total Eclipse of the Sun.**</u>

The path starts at dawn in the Pacific Ocean off the western coast of the United States.

This is when the umbra first touches the Earth. It makes its first landfall in Oregon at around 17:15 UT (10:15 am Pacific). Covering a path around 65 miles wide, the umbra will take just over 94 minutes to cross to the East coast (leaving South Carolina at around 18:49 UT (2:49 pm Eastern) before hurtling out into the Atlantic Ocean.

WEATHER REPORTS

As the day draws nearer, keep a close eye on weather reports and be prepared to move to somewhere else with a forecast of clearer skies if the weather in your town is cloudy or rainy. It's obviously important for the skies to be as clear as possible. See page 25 and 26 for more information on sourcing eclipse weather forecasts.

WHERE WILL YOU BE?

Decide whether you want to be amongst the crowds in a party atmosphere, or out in the wilderness with fewer distractions. It helps to be away from trees and tall buildings so there are few obstructions from your view of the sky. It also helps to be on higher ground, where you can watch the shadow approach and, after totality, observe as it shoots off into the distant horizon. It should be stunning to see from Oregon as it approaches from across the Pacific Ocean, or from South Carolina as it departs over the Atlantic Ocean. The path of totality traverses parts of Grand Teton National Park and Great Smoky Mountains National Park. Both locations would be spectacular.

BUT WHERE WITHIN THE PATH OF TOTALITY?

The duration of totality varies along the path of this United States eclipse from between 2 minutes at the coast in Oregon to a maximum of 2 minutes 40 seconds in Illinois.

The illustration on the following page shows the importance of choosing the right location with respect to the distance from the center line of the path. The umbra is oval in shape as it moves across the face of the earth, tracing a path about 65 miles wide.

A person located on the center line in Illinois would experience the Sun being blotted out totally for around 2 minutes 40 seconds. If you move away from this center line towards the northern or southern limit of the path, the length of time in totality starts to decrease.

Nearer the edge of the path, the duration of totality decreases rapidly, as illustrated by the decreasing lengths of the blue lines. I would recommend being within 20 miles on either side of the center line in order to experience a good long time under the shadow. In this example, taken from Illinois, you would be guaranteed 2 minutes or more of totality.

In Oregon, standing within 20 miles north or south of the center line would give you around 1 minute 30 seconds of totality. It's not essential to be located on the center line, but I recommend being within 20 miles of it.

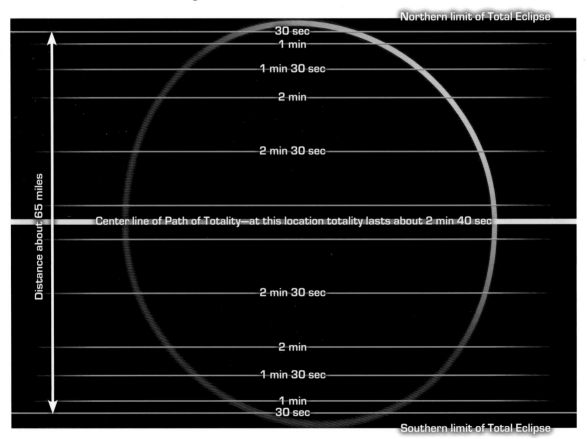

Distance about 65 miles

Northern limit of Total Eclipse

30 sec
1 min
1 min 30 sec
2 min
2 min 30 sec

Center line of Path of Totality—at this location totality lasts about 2 min 40 sec

2 min 30 sec
2 min
1 min 30 sec
1 min
30 sec

Southern limit of Total Eclipse

CITIES & TOWNS IN THE PATH OF TOTALITY (SORTED WEST TO EAST)

Town/city	State	Time zone	Start of partial eclipse	Start of totality	Duration of totality (City center)	End of partial eclipse
Lincoln City	OR	Pacific	9:04 am	10:16 am	1 min 54 sec	11:36 am
Salem	OR	Pacific	9:05 am	10:17 am	1 min 54 sec	11:37 am
Albany	OR	Pacific	9:05 am	10:17 am	1 min 51 sec	11:37 am
Baker City	OR	Pacific	9:09 am	10:24 am	1 min 35 sec	11:46 am
Idaho Falls	ID	Mountain	10:15 am	11:33 am	1 min 47 sec	12:58 pm
Jackson	WY	Mountain	10:16 am	11:34 am	2 min 15 sec	1.00 pm
Riverton	WY	Mountain	10:19 am	11:39 am	2 min 13 sec	1:05 pm
Casper	WY	Mountain	10:22 am	11:42 am	2 min 25 sec	1:09 pm
Alliance	NE	Mountain	10:27 am	11:49 am	2 min 30 sec	1:16 pm
North Platte	NE	Central	11:30 am	12:54 pm	1 min 45 sec	2:21 pm
Grand Island	NE	Central	11:34 am	12:58 pm	2 min 34 sec	2:26 pm
Lincoln	NE	Central	11:37 am	1:02 pm	1 min 16 sec	2:29 pm

CITIES & TOWNS IN THE PATH OF TOTALITY (SORTED WEST TO EAST)

Town/city	State	Time zone	Start of partial eclipse	Start of totality	Duration of totality (City center)	End of partial eclipse
Saint Joseph	MO	Central	11:40 am	1:06 pm	2 min 38 sec	2:34 pm
Kansas City	KS	Central	11:41 am	1:08 pm	28 sec	2:35 pm
Columbia	MO	Central	11:45 am	1:12 pm	2 min 37 sec	2:40 pm
Jefferson City	MO	Central	11:46 am	1:13 pm	2 min 29 sec	2:41 pm
Chester	IL	Central	11:51 am	1:18 pm	2 min 39 sec	2:46 pm
Carbondale	IL	Central	11:52 am	1:20 pm	2 min 37 sec	2:47 pm
Hopkinsville	KY	Central	11:56 am	1:24 pm	2 min 40 sec	2:51 pm
Nashville	TN	Central	11:58 am	1:27 pm	1 min 52 sec	2:54 pm
Crossville	TN	Central	12:02 pm	1:31 pm	2 min 32 sec	2:57 pm
Greenville	SC	Eastern	1:09 pm	2:38 pm	2 min 10 sec	4:02 pm
Columbia	SC	Eastern	1:13 pm	2:41 pm	2 min 30 sec	4:06 pm
Charleston	SC	Eastern	1:16 pm	2:46 pm	1 min 33 sec	4:10 pm

Everyone in the United States, Canada, Central America and the northern countries of South America will experience a partial eclipse of the Sun.

The maximum proportion of the Sun obscured by the Moon, and consequently the reduction in daylight, depends on how far you will be away from the path of totality. Los Angeles will experience around 70% maximum coverage while New Yorkers will see around a maximum of 80% of the Sun covered.

NASA View of the Earth showing the areas of partial eclipse on August 21, 2017. See map on the following page.

The path of totality (in deep blue) stretches from the Pacific Ocean to the Atlantic Ocean, crossing or touching fourteen States.

The lines (in pale blue) running parallel to this path show the extent of the penumbra and the percentage of the Sun's diameter which is obscured when the eclipse is at its maximum.

The time lines at half hour intervals (in green) give the time (UT) when the eclipse is at its maximum.

Note that some maps may contain times in UT (Universal Time).

- to convert UT to **Pacific**, subtract 7 hours
- to convert UT to **Mountain**, subtract 6 hours
- to convert UT to **Central**, subtract 5 hours
- to convert UT to **Eastern**, subtract 4 hours.

MAXIMUM PERCENTAGE OF SUN OBSCURED IN 10 LARGEST US CITIES

City	% Obscuration (% of Sun obscured by Moon)
New York City	72%
Los Angeles	62%
Chicago	87%
Houston	73%
Philadelphia	75%
Phoenix	63%
San Antonio	61%
San Diego	65%
Dallas	75%
San Jose	74%

MAXIMUM PERCENTAGE OF SUN OBSCURED IN MAJOR CITIES IN OTHER COUNTRIES

Country	City	% Obscuration (% of Sun obscured by Moon)
Canada	Montreal	58%
Canada	Toronto	70%
Canada	Vancouver	86%
Colombia	Bogotá	24%
Cuba	Havana	66%
Guatemala	Guatemala City	25%
Mexico	Mexico City	27%
Puerto Rico	San Juan	80%
Venezuela	Caracas	53%

Advice from experienced eclipse-watchers: if this is your first eclipse, just watch and enjoy it all. Photographing an eclipse is an art, and unless you really know what you are doing, results can be very disappointing. You might have no worthwhile pictures after spending the whole time looking at the screen or through a lens when you could have been absorbing the whole experience. There will be loads of excellent photographs published by the experts after the event.

To ancient peoples, the Sun was the source of all light and warmth and hence the source of all life, as it surely is. It was regarded as a deity and worshipped and often held a leading place in their mythologies. Any apparent threat to this giver-of-all-life was taken very seriously. It must have been terrifying for them to watch as some invisible creature took a bite out of the Sun and slowly consumed it entirely. To many peoples, an eclipse was a sign of the displeasure of the gods. To others, it foretold of some great disaster such as war, pestilence, famine or the death of kings.

For example, the Chippewa tribe of North America fired flaming arrows towards the Sun during an eclipse in an attempt to re-light the flames.

The Greeks believed that the gods were angry. The word "eclipse" derives from the ancient Greek *ekleipsis* meaning "abandonment, darkening, or cease to exist."

In ancient Mesopotamia, it was believed that a king would die and a terrible flood would follow when an eclipse occurred. And in ancient Mexico, they thought that the Sun and Moon were quarrelling, but in Tahiti, they believed that they were making love!

In India, it was believed that the beheaded Hindu god, Rahu, ate the Sun, but it would always reappear through his severed throat.

Other stories which blame various mythical creatures for devouring the Sun include an evil spirit toad (Vietnam); dragons (China); a giant bird (Hungary); sky wolf (Vikings); and a giant bear (Siberia).

People would do whatever they could to scare these invisible creatures away. They shouted, beat drums, pinched their children to make them cry, and hit their dogs to make them howl. And it works—the Sun has always returned so far!

A FEW DIMENSIONS

To give you an idea of the relative sizes of the Sun, the Earth and the Moon, imagine a football field. At one goal post is the Sun, a giant beach ball about 3 feet (90cm) in diameter. At the other goal post is a pea. A peppercorn is circling the pea at a distance of about 1 foot (30cm).

The pea represents the Earth and the peppercorn, the Moon. Another reason why total solar eclipses are rare!

In reality the sizes are a bit bigger:

- The diameter of the Sun is 865,000 miles (1,392,000 kilometers).
- The diameter of the Earth is 7,920 miles (12,740 kilometers).
- The diameter of the Moon is 2,160 miles (3,480 kilometers).
- The Earth is on average 93,000,000 miles (150,000,000 kilometers) from the Sun.
- The Moon is on average 238,860 miles (384,400 kilometers) from the Earth.
- The ratios of the diameters of Sun:Earth:Moon are about 400:4:1.

INTERESTING LITTLE TIDBITS ABOUT ECLIPSES

- The longest duration of totality for any solar eclipse is just over 7 minutes when viewed from ground level. The maximum on this occasion will be 2 minutes 40 seconds.
- In 1973, totality lasted much longer for passengers on a special supersonic Concorde flight which stayed in the Moon's shadow for a record of 74 minutes. On July 11, 2010, a chartered Airbus remained within the umbral shadow of a total solar eclipse for 9 minutes and 23 seconds.
- Street lights may well switch on automatically as light levels fall. It's interesting to see, but I recommend being away from street lights to experience this spectacular event.
- The eclipse will be featured on live TV. Bear in mind, however, that unless you are

in the exact same location as the TV camera, the images and commentary will be "out of sync" with your own experience. This is an event that you just have to *be there* to witness.

- It takes around 2 minutes for the Sun (or the Moon) to appear to move its own diameter across the sky!

TOTAL SOLAR ECLIPSES - THE NEXT 10 YEARS

2019 July 2	2020 December 14	2021 December 4	2024 April 8	2026 August 12	2027 August 2
Southern Pacific Ocean	Southern Pacific Ocean	Antarctica	Mexico	Arctic	Morocco
Chile	Chile		Central United States	Greenland	Spain
Argentina	Argentina		Eastern Canada	Iceland	Algeria
	Southern Atlantic Ocean			Spain	Libya
					Egypt

JARGON BUSTER

Baily's Beads

Just before totality, the last rays of the Sun shining between the mountains of the Moon appear as a bright string of beads. These are known as Baily's Beads after the English astronomer, Francis Baily, who described the effect in 1836. They can be seen again as the Sun reappears after totality.

Obscuration

The percentage area of the Sun obscured by the Moon.

Chromosphere

(literally sphere of color) The lower atmosphere of the Sun. It appears as a thin red crescent for a few seconds at the beginning and end of totality.

Corona

The outermost regions of the Sun's atmosphere. During totality, the visible area appears as a halo around the Sun.

Totality

The time when the Sun is completely covered by the Moon.

Penumbra

The area of partial shadow of the Moon where only part of the light from the Sun is blocked out. An observer in the penumbra sees a partial eclipse of the Sun.

Partial Eclipse

An observer sees the Sun reduced to a crescent shape as it is partially obscured by the Moon. The observer is located within the penumbra (partial shadow).

Umbra

The part of the Moon's shadow where all of the light from the Sun is blocked out. An observer in the umbra sees a Total Eclipse of the Sun.

Prominences

These are flame-colored projections of hot ionized gas rising from the surface of the Sun. We should see them during totality.

The Path of Totality

The path followed by the umbra as it travels across the face of the Earth.

24

USEFUL WEB LINKS

pamhine.com	Author's website has all the following links
mascotbooks.com	Publisher's website
eclipse.gsfc.nasa.gov/eclipse.html	NASA's eclipse site
greatamericaneclipse.com	Extensive resources
eclipse2017.org	More extensive resources
eclipsewise.com	For eclipse predictions
mreclipse.com	For eclipse photography
eclipsophile.com	Jay Anderson's expert weather information

ACKNOWLEDGMENTS

Special thanks to Fred Espenak and NASA.

The data on the foldout map belongs to ©2016 Google.

iStock Photos

page 2	United States Highway Map	Crossroadscreative

Scan this QR code to access a **YouTube video** in which the author explains in simple terms what will happen and why it's so important to get yourself to the **Path of Totality** on Monday, August 21, 2017. SAVE THE DATE!

Scan this QR code to go to the author's website: *2017totaleclipse.com.*

NOTES

Where were you? Who was with you? How was the weather? How did it make you feel?

_____

_____

_____

_____

_____

_____

_____

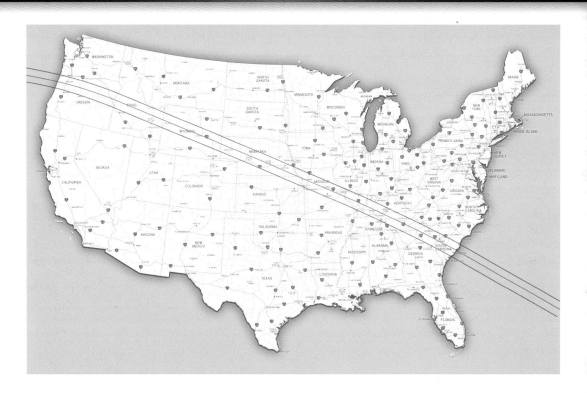

The attached fold-out map is marked with timings at 5 minute intervals along the path of totality. Each label details:

- the time (in local time) of the start of totality at that location
- the duration of totality
- the start of the partial phase of the eclipse.

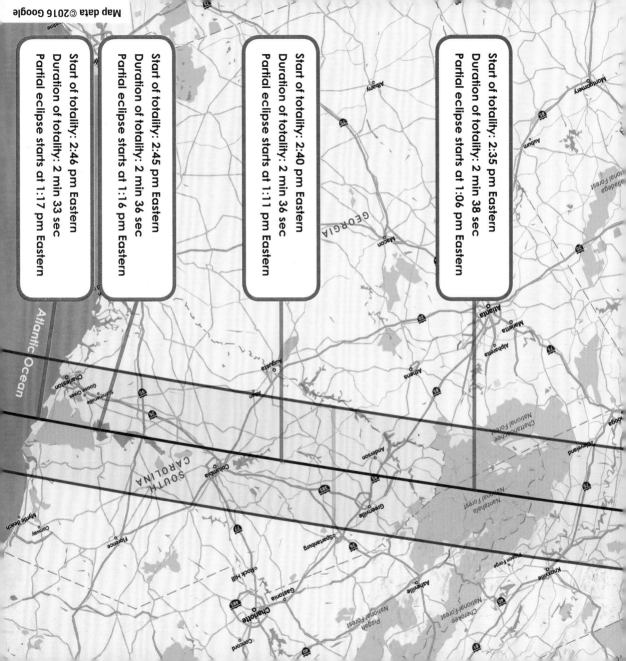

Start of totality: 2:35 pm Eastern
Duration of totality: 2 min 38 sec
Partial eclipse starts at 1:06 pm Eastern

Start of totality: 2:40 pm Eastern
Duration of totality: 2 min 36 sec
Partial eclipse starts at 1:11 pm Eastern

Start of totality: 2:45 pm Eastern
Duration of totality: 2 min 36 sec
Partial eclipse starts at 1:16 pm Eastern

Start of totality: 2:46 pm Eastern
Duration of totality: 2 min 33 sec
Partial eclipse starts at 1:17 pm Eastern

Map data © 2016 Google

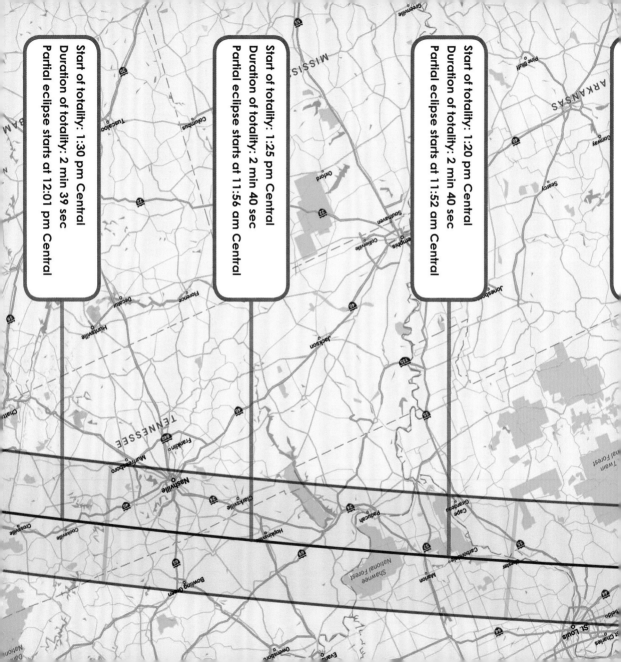

Start of totality: 1:20 pm Central
Duration of totality: 2 min 40 sec
Partial eclipse starts at 11:52 am Central

Start of totality: 1:25 pm Central
Duration of totality: 2 min 40 sec
Partial eclipse starts at 11:56 am Central

Start of totality: 1:30 pm Central
Duration of totality: 2 min 39 sec
Partial eclipse starts at 12:01 pm Central

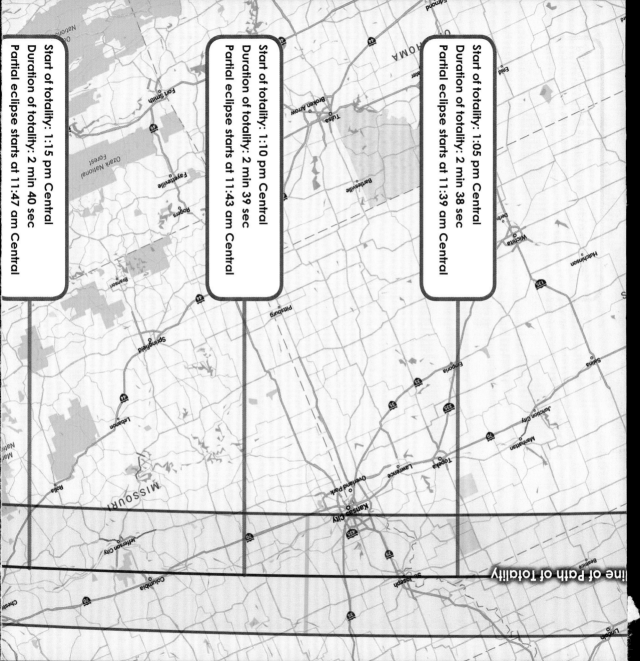

Start of totality: 1:05 pm Central
Duration of totality: 2 min 38 sec
Partial eclipse starts at 11:39 am Central

Start of totality: 1:10 pm Central
Duration of totality: 2 min 39 sec
Partial eclipse starts at 11:43 am Central

Start of totality: 1:15 pm Central
Duration of totality: 2 min 40 sec
Partial eclipse starts at 11:47 am Central

Line of Path of Totality